THE
WITCHES
OF VENICE

written and illustrated by

Beni Montresor

Alfred A. Knopf

New York

To J., who knows how to fly in the skies of Venice

L. C. Catalog card number: 63-9114

THIS IS A BORZOI BOOK PUBLISHED BY ALFRED A. KNOPF, INC.

In the ancient city of Venice there once lived a king of great
power and a queen covered with jewels from head to foot.
But they had no son to inherit their throne, and so they fretted
and could not sleep well at all.

The situation was intolerable. The King of Venice thought
and thought, and finally he summoned all the philosophers
of the world. They arrived with great speed. After days and
days of discussion they said: "We are sorry, Your Majesty, but
we have no solution."

Then one day two Fairies of the Lagoon came to the King. "*We* have a solution, Your Majesty," they said sweetly, and held out to him a leafy plant. Then they sang:

Plant this in your garden
And when it blooms at dawn,
You will find, to your surprise,
A little child is born.

"Silly creatures! Children aren't born from plants!" roared the King, and he threw the plant out of the window.

The next morning the kitchenmaid was sweeping the courtyard. When she saw the plant, half dried up and almost dead, she said, "A plant is to be planted"—and she planted it in the middle of the kitchen garden.

After a while the Sun came out and warmed the poor plant, and suddenly it blossomed. The Sun beamed with joy and asked, "How are you now, my little one?"

Out of the plant hopped a beautiful little boy, merry and rosy-cheeked—and the little boy replied, "Much better, thank you, dear Sun."

The kitchenmaid, who was at the window, saw everything. She ran to the throne room and exclaimed, "Your Majesty, a little boy has come out of the plant!"

"Liar!" roared the King, but he added, "Let us go and see."

They went to the kitchen garden, and when they were standing in front of the little boy, the maid said, "You see? It is a boy."

"It is a plant!" screamed the stubborn King.

"Viva the King! You are the King; you know everything," the kitchenmaid exclaimed with admiration.

Then solemnly the King of Venice decreed: "Because this
plant is a plant, it must remain planted in the kitchen garden."
He called for twelve guards and put them all around
the garden wall so that the little boy could not even try
to escape.

The Sun came in every day and made the juiciest fruits in
the world grow for the little boy. The Wind came, too, and
hoping to amuse him, sent leaves spinning into the air.

But it was useless, for not even the beginning of a smile
appeared on the child's face.

Time passed. Then one day the Wind rushed to the little
boy and whispered, "Hide! Hide! Witches are coming!"

Into that kitchen garden, no one knows through what hole or
crack or cranny, there came dancing two of the Witches of the
Grand Canal.

"We've come to see what the little flower-plant boy is like," they said, and they searched above and below every leaf, but all in vain.

"You forgot to look into the watering can," called the kitchenmaid from the window.

The witches pulled the little boy out of the watering can; they studied him at length. "Oh!" they exclaimed, "he has two sad eyes, just like our little flower-plant girl. How tiresome!"

Then they danced over to the window and said to the kitchenmaid, "Tell the King and Queen they are invited to our gay Summer Ball."

"What little flower-plant girl?" the child called, but the witches had already danced away.

From that day on the little flower-plant boy thought of nothing but the little flower-plant girl.

So one morning the little boy gathered all the dry branches in the kitchen garden, and he built a big pigeon, hollow inside and with two wheels attached to its feet.

"Wind," said the little boy, "we are leaving. I am going to find the little flower-plant girl, and with her I will invent wonderful games."

"What about the King?" whispered the Wind.

"The King doesn't like flower-plant children," answered the little boy, and he climbed inside the pigeon. The Wind pushed the pigeon to the gate of the kitchen garden; but there stood the King's guards keeping watch.

The Wind whirled around and around until the guards' eyes were filled with dust, and then the pigeon slipped through the gate.

At last the little boy was free!

Blowing and puffing, the Wind pushed the pigeon across the entire city of Venice, but no one saw it because all around floated the clouds of dust raised by the Wind.

At twilight they arrived at the great palace of the Witches of the Grand Canal. The Wind was trembling with fear.

"Ch-child," he stammered, "now tell me how we are to get in."

The little boy crawled out of the pigeon and turned the handle of the palace door. The door creaked open. The witches had forgotten to lock it!

He got back into the pigeon, and the Wind began to blow again . . . and then the pigeon slipped inside the great palace of the Witches of the Grand Canal.

It was the very evening of the witches' great Summer Ball. The witches were up in their bedrooms busily dressing, and on the ground floor there was not a soul to be seen.

The little boy began his search of the palace's one hundred rooms. From a hole in the pigeon's side he carefully inspected each nook and cranny.

He could find no trace of the little flower-plant girl on the ground floor. The Wind pushed the pigeon down to the wine cellars, and there, out of the darkness, stumbled a dragon.

"Oh! Oh!" gasped the Wind. "He will eat us!"

"How handsome I am! Quite a beauty!" the dragon was saying, admiring his reflection in a mirror.

"Have you seen the little flower-plant girl?" asked the little boy from inside the pigeon.

"I haven't eaten her, if that's what you mean," answered the dragon. "Only beautiful princesses are fine enough for me to eat." Moving on he began again: "How handsome I am! Quite a beauty!"

"But have you heard of her?" the little boy called after him.

"Oh, some time ago the Witch Mother spoke to me of a little flower-plant girl. But she is rather eccentric and tends to exaggerate," replied the dragon over his shoulder.

The little boy turned the pigeon around, and the Wind pushed it back to the ground floor and then up the grand staircase. Hurrying down was an enormous ogre, carrying twenty-one bottles of wine under each arm.

"Have you seen the little flower-plant girl?" the little boy asked.

"I have no time to answer!" grumbled the ogre, and he rushed away.

"No one has seen her . . . ." said the little boy to the Wind.

They started down a long corridor. . .

Darkness had fallen, and downstairs the ball was about to begin. Gondolas filled with guests were arriving at the palace gates; finally the King and the Queen of Venice arrived, covered with gold and precious jewels. Everyone in Venice had crowded around to see Their Majesties; and when they appeared everyone exclaimed, "Such beauty! Such splendor!"

More than anything else in the world, the Witches of the
Grand Canal loved dancing. That night, at the thought of
so many people to dance with, they were particularly excited.

There was a flourish of trumpets, and the witches chanted
their greeting to their guests:

> *We, graceful Witches*
> *Of the Grand Canal,*
> *Graciously say to you—*
> *Come feasting, come dancing,*
> *And soon you will see*
> *How lovely, how thrilling*
> *The whole world will be.*

And all began to dance with such gaiety as had never before
been seen.

Up on the second floor the little boy had finished searching
the witches' parlors and was climbing to the third floor. . .

Up there were the twenty-seven bedrooms of the elder witches. The little boy looked under every bed and inside every wig, but he found nothing.

Downstairs the witches sounded gayer than ever. Their shrieks of delight could be heard for miles around as they danced and danced. The little boy climbed still higher.

On the fourth floor were the thirty-three bedrooms of the younger witches. The child spent hours and hours rummaging through the mountains of ball gowns left over from their parties. But still there was no sign of the little flower-plant girl.

The Wind and the little boy climbed up to the palace tower, and there at the head of the stairs was a closed door. On the door was written, "Witch Mother."

"Don't go inside! She sucks blood and spits poison!" wailed the Wind, getting ready to leave.

"Perhaps the little girl is kept prisoner in there, and the Witch Mother beats her," said the little boy.

With a sob the Wind said, "Oh, poor little prisoner"—and blew the door wide open.

The Witch Mother was swooping around the room on a broomstick, shrieking, "I am the great Witch Mother!"

"Excuse me, Madam, have you seen a little flower-plant girl?" the little boy asked.

"Don't bother me!" shouted the Witch Mother. "Go downstairs and dance with my foolish daughters!" Then even more furiously, she swooped and she shrieked, "Get out! The sky of Venice is all mine!"

Sadly the little boy started back to the ground floor. He had searched ninety-nine rooms, ninety-nine rooms and not one less, and not the slightest trace had he found of the little flower-plant girl.

Only the ballroom was left to be searched. But how could she possibly be hidden in a room filled with all those dancing people?

When they were outside the ballroom, the little boy said, "Dear Wind, open the door."

"That door!" The Wind could hardly utter a sound. So great was his fear of the witches that he collapsed against the door — and it sprang open.

The pigeon appeared triumphantly at the ballroom entrance; everyone was struck dumb by the sight.

When they had recovered a little bit from the shock, the witches whispered to each other, "Mother is at it again. She has put herself inside that pigeon and come down to spoil our fun. Ignore her."

As for the King and Queen and the courtiers, they said haughtily, "It is clear that these silly witches are trying to impress us with a homemade wooden pigeon. Ridiculous! It should at least have been made of gold."

And so, very displeased, they too ignored the pigeon, and they all went back to their dancing with even more abandon than before.

At last the little boy could begin his inspection of the ballroom.

The Wind pushed the pigeon among the dancers. The little
boy looked here and he looked there; he looked under chairs
and under tables, but at last the pigeon had stepped on the feet
of too many people.

"Away, pigeon!" they cried. "Away from here!" and they
pushed the pigeon into a corner.

"The little girl is lost forever," thought the little boy, "and I
will never play wonderful games with her. Now I am the
only little flower-plant child in the whole world."

The dancers were whirling about the room at the peak of
their gaiety, and inside the pigeon the little boy was crying.

But all of a sudden. . . .

The crystal pendants of the chandelier began to tinkle; then they tinkled louder; and then the sound was almost music.

The little boy looked up. Oh, marvel! Among those glittering pendants he saw a tiny hand, and the tiny hand was jingling the pendants to signal him.

It was the little flower-plant girl! She was in the chandelier! The witches had thought, "People rarely put little girls in chandeliers, so let us put her up there, and no one will ever suspect where she is."

"Who are you?" the little girl whispered from above.

"Shh! I've come to free you!" answered the little boy.

"Oh, thank you!" she said.

Then the little boy told the Wind, "Blow, blow!" and the Wind blew with all the breath that he had in him, and King and Queen and witches and courtiers all went tumbling with feet high in the air.

The little boy lowered the chandelier and helped the little girl out, and they jumped into the pigeon. Just then dawn broke, and jubilantly the Sun appeared and made the dry branches of the pigeon burst into leaf.

Then the pigeon stretched his leafy green wings and flew away through the window.

"What has happened?" demanded the witches and the King and Queen, getting back on their feet. But no one knew what to answer, because really that night they had danced too much and too long and their poor heads were entirely befuddled.

The pigeon carried the little girl and the little boy high
into the glorious sky of Venice, soaring and diving and
circling—and their good friends the Sun and the Wind were
with them. And this was indeed one of the wonderful games
that only little flower-plant children can play.

Text set in Monotype Century Schoolbook. Composed at H. O. Bullard, New York City. Printed by Reehl Litho, New York City. Bound by Economy Bookbinding Corp., Kearny, New Jersey. Typography by Beni Montresor and Atha Tehon.